AMAZING SCIENCE

Facts, Feats & Puzzles

by Dan Nevins

Watermill Press

AMAZING SCIENCE FACTS, FEATS & PUZZLES

Published by Watermill Press, an imprint and registered trademark of
Troll Communications L.L.C.

Copyright © 1995 by Troll Communications L.L.C.

Printed in the United States of America.

10   9   8   7   6   5   4

WELCOME!

In this fascinating book you'll discover amazing science facts and feats. And you can enjoy all kinds of brain-bending puzzles. So grab a pencil and have some fun! If you get stumped, the answer pages begin on page 60.

THE HUMAN BODY IS HOTTER THAN THE SUN?

Pound for pound, a human being produces *more* heat than the sun! Only because of its size does the sun emit so much heat. If the sun's mass and a human's mass could be made equal, *we* would generate more heat!

HOW LARGE THE SUN IS?

The sun could hold about 1,300,000 earths.

HOW MUCH A PERSON WOULD WEIGH ON THE SUN?

Because of the sun's extreme gravity, a person would weigh about 2 tons (1.8 metric tons).

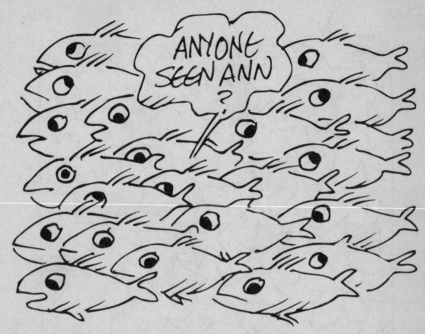

WHAT'S AMAZING ABOUT THE COD?

The cod produces an incredible number of eggs. If all the eggs laid by a single 75-pound (34-kg) cod developed into adults, the ocean would become quite crowded. That's because a 21-pound (10-kg) cod can lay up to 9,000,000 eggs in one spawning period!

WHAT'S UNUSUAL ABOUT THE ELECTRIC EEL?

Adult electric eels are blind. To find their food, they give off a small electrical discharge. Then they produce an electric field of up to 650 volts to stun or kill their prey.

Across

1. Pushcart with one wheel (rhymes with marrow).
9. Brother's daughter.
10. Catcher's glove.
12. _ _ _ _ the truth.
14. He, she, or _ _.
15. Nickname for an elevated subway.
16. Sixth musical note.
17. To droop (rhymes with bag).
19. Opposite of yes.
20. One of Santa's helpers.
22. Lone Ranger's friend.
23. Canadian territory.
25. Public-transportation vehicle.
27. Every car has a steering _ _ _ _ _.
28. Abbreviation for promissory note.

Down

2. Picnic pest.
3. Religious ceremonies (rhymes with nights).
4. Abbreviation for real estate.
5. Eight-sided figure.
6. Tiny (rhymes with be).
7. We inflated many _ _ _ _ _ _ _ _ for the birthday party.
8. Grin.
11. Mediterranean nation shaped like a boot.
13. Loaned.
18. Coral island (rhymes with play goal).
21. To give off smoke (rhymes with spume).
24. Abbreviation for black and white.
25. Abbreviation for boiling point.
26. Short for United Nations.

WHO THE GREATEST INVENTOR OF ALL TIME IS?

Thomas Alva Edison is perhaps the greatest inventor who ever lived. He obtained 1,300 patents on his inventions. In one four-year period, he averaged one patent about every five days!

WHO DISCOVERED VACCINATION?

The word vaccination comes from the Latin word *vacca*, or cow. In the late 1700s an English doctor, Edward Jenner, took some infected tissue from the sore of a milkmaid infected with cowpox, a disease of cows. He rubbed the sample into a scratch in another person's skin. This was the first reliable inoculation against the dreaded disease smallpox.

Fit the names of these famous scientists and thinkers into the puzzle. We've filled in one name to get you started.

4 letters
ROSS (English physician)

5 letters
GAMOW (Russian-born American physicist)
GAUSS (German mathematician and astronomer)
MORSE (American inventor)

6 letters
DARWIN (English naturalist)
EDISON (American inventor)
EUCLID (Greek mathematician and physicist)
JENNER (English physician)

7 letters
FARADAY (English physicist and chemist)
PASTEUR (French chemist)
PAULING (American chemist)
PTOLEMY (Greek-Egyptian astronomer and geographer)

10 letters
COPERNICUS (Polish astronomer)

11 letters
ARISTARCHUS (Greek astronomer)

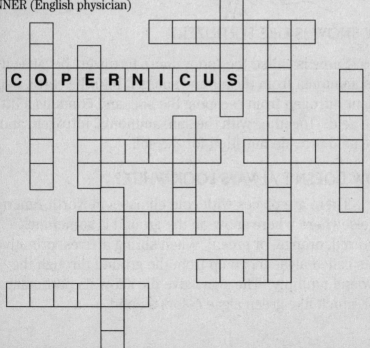

WHY SNOW IS LIKE FERTILIZER?

Snow is called the "poor man's fertilizer" because it traps ammonia from the air and soaks it into the earth, helps prevent nitrogen from escaping the soil, and contains a little nitric acid. Together with the sun, ammonia, nitrogen, and nitric acid provide nutrition for the soil.

SNOW DOESN'T ALWAYS LOOK WHITE?

There are places with cold climates in North America and elsewhere where snow on the ground is sometimes tinted red, orange, or green! When spring arrives, primitive plants called algae move up from the ground through the snow and multiply. The algae give the snow its particular color, much like green algae colors a pond.

Can you draw each figure making one continuous line —
without lifting your pencil, crossing a line, or retracing a
line?

Atoms

Crystal

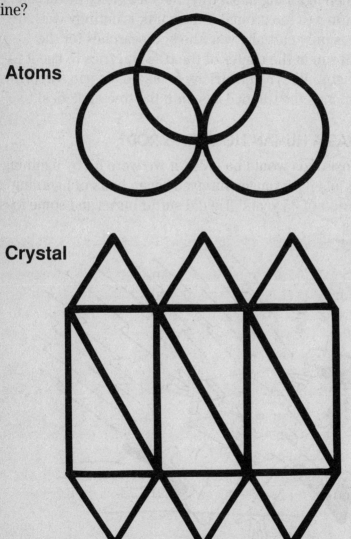

HOW LIGHTNING EXPLODES A TREE?

When lightning hits a tree, the electricity travels all the way down to the ground if the trunk is entirely wet. If the trunk is only partially wet, the bolt searches for the channel of sap in the center of the tree and tries to use it to reach the ground. The electricity heats up the sap, vaporizes it, and expands the trapped gas until the tree explodes!

THERE WAS A HUMAN LIGHTNING ROD?

Most of us would be killed if we were hit by lightning. But a Virginia park ranger survived seven bolts of lightning over a period of 35 years! He did suffer burns and some loss of hearing.

Find and circle the hidden science words. Look up, down, across, diagonally, and backward.

AIR	GAS	THUNDER
ATMOSPHERE	MINERAL	VAPOR
BACTERIA	ODOR	VIRUS
BOLT	OZONE	WATER
CHEMICAL	TEMPERATURE	

```
E  S  A  G  X  D  I  Q  A  A  A
G  R  P  A  T  L  Y  J  I  T  I
T  H  U  N  D  E  R  R  W  M  R
Z  R  E  T  A  W  I  S  F  O  E
L  B  D  E  A  K  U  B  D  S  T
R  O  F  J  R  R  Z  O  O  P  C
O  L  A  C  I  M  E  H  C  H  A
P  T  N  V  H  X  G  P  R  E  B
A  I  O  Z  O  N  E  L  M  R  S
V  T  P  F  V  T  S  V  X  E  O
M  I  N  E  R  A  L  Q  I  Y  T
```

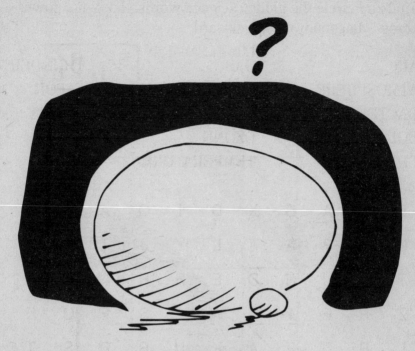

WHICH BIRD LAYS THE TINIEST EGGS?

The hummingbird. It would take about 125 hummingbird eggs to equal the weight of a single hen's egg.

WHICH BIRD IMITATES OTHERS?

The mockingbird is famed for its ability to imitate the calls of other birds. One naturalist in South Carolina witnessed a mockingbird making 32 different bird calls in ten minutes!

Do this puzzle like a regular crossword. But instead of filling in squares, put one letter in each triangle. For example, fill in the word BIRD like this:

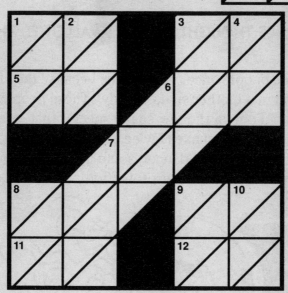

Across

1. High-school graduation dance.
3. Pierce with a knife (rhymes with crab).
5. Final word of a prayer.
6. Wild West outlaw: _ _ _ _ _ the Kid.
7. Not warm.
8. Begin.
9. Sharpen (rhymes with loan).
11. Word for music, painting, theater, and so on.
12. Church seats.

Down

1. British nickname for baby carriage (rhymes with gram).
2. Prophetic sign (rhymes with Roman).
3. Quiet (rhymes with hill).
4. These shoes fit very COMFORT_ _ _ _.
6. Cowboy's foot covering.
7. Light, usually two-wheeled vehicles (rhymes with parts).
8. Heavenly body.
9. Desire; wish for (rhymes with rope).
10. Everyday events.

WHAT'S UNUSUAL ABOUT RATTLESNAKES?

Rattlers are deaf and depend on vibrations to alert them to prey or enemies. Also, they can swim and climb trees!

PEOPLE ONCE THOUGHT SNAKES SWALLOWED THEIR YOUNG?

Some people once thought this because they found baby snakes in a mother snake's body. These people may have observed one of the few snake species that give birth to live young. (Most snakes lay eggs.) Another explanation could be that in times of danger, some baby snakes jump into their mother's mouth for protection!

Fit these snake names and words into the puzzle. We've filled in one name to get you started.

3 letters
ASP
BOA
PIT

4 letters
CORN
FANG

5 letters
COBRA
MAMBA
VENOM
VIPER

6 letters
PYTHON
RATTLE

7 letters
HOGNOSE

10 letters
COPPERHEAD
SIDEWINDER

11 letters
CONSTRICTOR

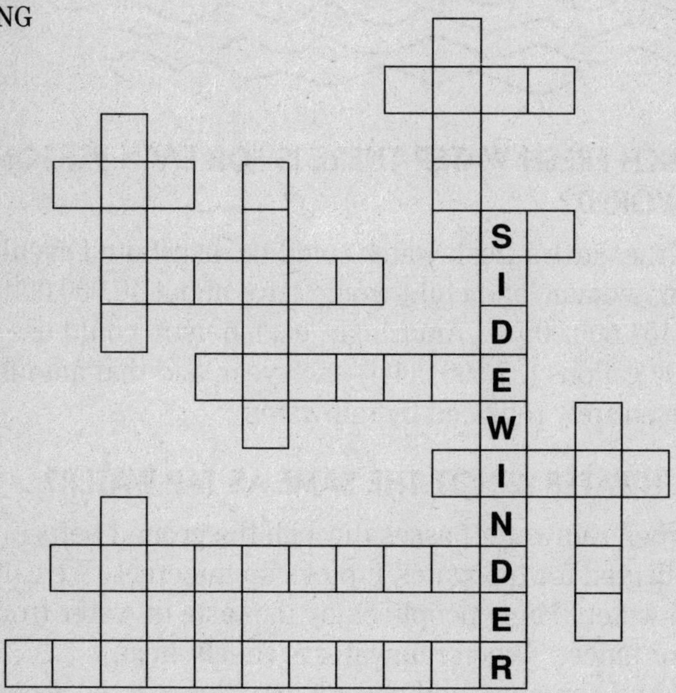

HOW MUCH FRESH WATER THERE IS FOR EACH PERSON IN THE WORLD?

If the earth's fresh water could be distributed evenly, each man, woman, and child would have about 40,000,000 gallons (151,600,000 l). Amazingly, each person could use 10,000,000 gallons (37,900,000 l) each year, and that amount would be entirely replaced by rainwater.

WHY RAINWATER IS NOT THE SAME AS TAP WATER?

When rainwater passes through the ground before being collected for tap water, it picks up minerals. We call this hard water. Many people enjoy the taste of water from the tap, or faucet. When rainwater is caught in an aboveground container and doesn't pass through the ground, it has few minerals and is called soft water. Soft water doesn't taste as good to many people, but it is fine for washing hair or clothes.

Change only one letter in each word to spell 12 new words associated with WATER.

1. SALLY   _____ _____ _____ _____ _____

2. PAIN   _____ _____ _____ _____

3. SHOW   _____ _____ _____ _____

4. WAKE   _____ _____ _____ _____

5. HIDE   _____ _____ _____ _____

6. PEA   _____ _____ _____

7. ACE   _____ _____ _____

8. VALOR   _____ _____ _____ _____ _____

9. CARD   _____ _____ _____ _____

10. LOFT   _____ _____ _____ _____

11. WEB   _____ _____ _____

12. STRING   _____ _____ _____ _____ _____ _____

THE DIFFERENCE BETWEEN A CYCLONE AND A TORNADO?

A cyclone can sometimes cover an area up to half the size of the United States! A tornado is a much smaller but intense cyclone that usually is only 300 yards (273 m) across. Low atmospheric pressure at the center and winds spiraling inward are the two characteristics of a cyclone. These storms are called hurricanes when they take place in the Atlantic Ocean and typhoons when they happen in the Pacific Ocean.

WHAT A TSUNAMI IS?

Waves are generally created by winds or tides. A *tsunami*, however, is a huge wave formed by an earthquake or volcanic eruption on the ocean floor. This "tidal wave" can reach a height of 100 feet (30.5 m) or more and race faster than 200 miles (322 km) per hour.

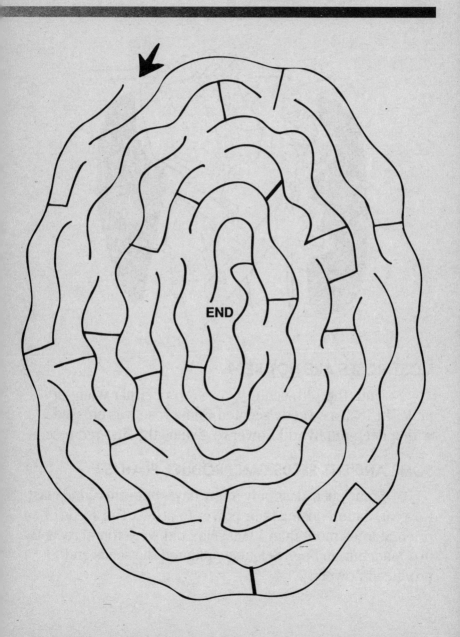

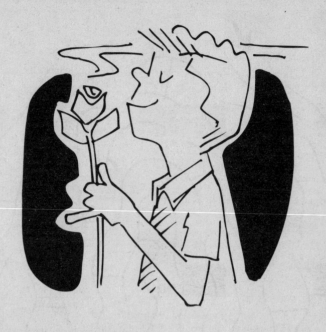

MOST ROSES ARE <u>NOT</u> RED?

Until the 19th century, roses were either white or pink. In 1832 a sweetly scented China rose was crossed with a deep-red hybrid flower to give us the first red rose.

SOME ANCIENT SEEDS CAN PRODUCE PLANTS?

Some seeds last only a few days, but other kinds last for years before losing their power to grow. The seeds of an oriental lotus more than 1,000 years old were found recently in a Manchurian bog. Scientists planted the seeds and produced flowers!

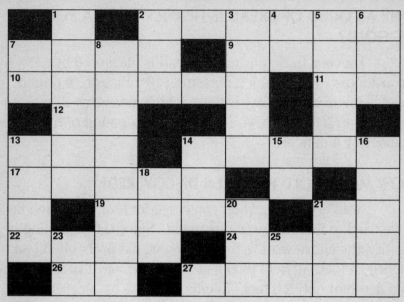

Across

2. _ _ _ _ _ _ Doodle Dandy.
7. Too.
9. Nice, N _ _ _ _, Nicest.
10. Planet known for its many rings.
11. Abbreviation for Los Angeles.
12. Abbreviation for North America.
13. Only one _ _ _ customer (rhymes with fur).
14. Sharp part of a rose.
17. Minklike animal that loves to swim.
19. Underwater ridge made of coral.
21. He, she, _ _.
22. Give off a bad smell (rhymes with beak).
24. President _ _ _ _ L D Reagan.
26. Short for all right.
27. An entire quantity.

Down

1. Earth is one.
2. Not I, but _ _ _.
3. Before the tenth.
4. Abbreviation for Kansas City.
5. One who fishes for a snakelike fish (rhymes with dealer).
6. Abbreviation for earned run average.
7. Abbreviation for Anglo-Saxon.
8. Popular TV space show.
13. Not rich.
14. Maple, oak, and pine are different kinds of _ _ _ E S.
15. Opposite of off.
16. Pertaining to birth (rhymes with fatal).
18. An exclamation used by some people when they see a mouse.
20. To and _ _ _.
21. Deposit your money _ _ _ savings account.
23. As bright as a N _ _ N sign.
25. Abbreviation for overtime.

WHY A POUND OF BREAD IS HEAVIER THAN A POUND OF GOLD?

This is a trick question. Bread is measured by avoirdupois weight, which measures 16 ounces to a pound. Gold is measured by troy weight, which measures 12 ounces to a pound. Therefore, you can say that a pound of bread is heavier by 4 ounces!

HOW MUCH GOLD HAS BEEN DISCOVERED?

Not very much, when you consider how many people have tried to find this precious metal. Since the beginning of history, the entire world's production would probably fill an American football field (300 feet x 160 feet, or 91 m x 49 m) to a depth of only 2.6 feet (79 cm).

Fit the names of these elements into the puzzle. We've filled in one element to get you started.

3 letters
TIN

4 letters
GOLD
IRON
NEON
ZINC

6 letters
COBALT
COPPER
ERBIUM
HELIUM
IODINE
RADIUM
SULFUR

7 letters
ARSENIC
IRIDIUM
URANIUM

8 letters
ANTIMONY
NITROGEN
THALLIUM

9 letters
YTTERBIUM

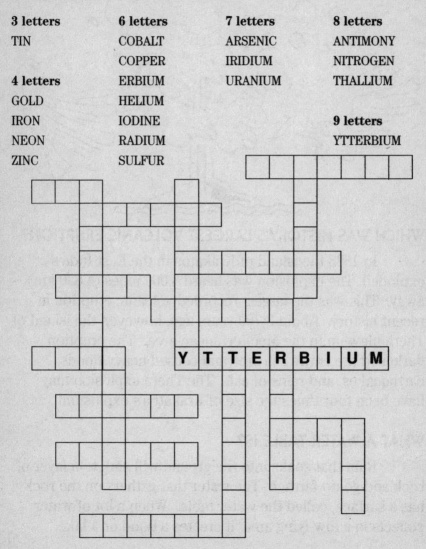

WHICH WAS HISTORY'S LARGEST VOLCANIC ERUPTION?

In 1883 the island of Krakatoa in the East Indies exploded. The explosion was heard 3,000 miles (4,830 km) away. This was the largest recorded volcanic eruption in recent history. About 3,700 years ago, however, the island of Thera blew up in the Mediterranean area. The eruption darkened the entire sea area and caused heavy floods, earthquakes, and rains of ash. The Thera explosion may have been four times the size of Krakatoa's explosion!

WHAT A WATER TABLE IS?

Rain that soaks into the ground will sink to a layer of rock and go no farther. The water that gathers on the rock has a surface, called the water table. When a lot of water collects in a low-lying area, it creates a pond or a lake.

Arrange the numbers 14, 16, 17, 18, and 20 in the circles so the sum of the numbers of each straight line is 40. Use each number only once.

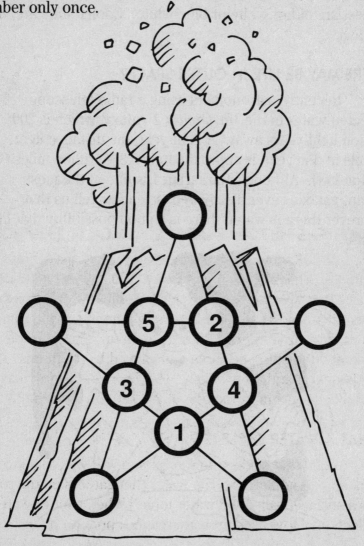

STARS ARE DIFFERENT COLORS?

Temperature determines the color of stars. The hottest are either white or blue-white. Cooler stars are reddish.

THERE MAY BE LIFE IN OUTER SPACE?

Recently, astronomers using a radio telescope detected water in the *Markarian 1* galaxy, which is 200 million light-years away. A light-year, the distance light travels in one year, is approximately 5.878 trillion miles (9.46 trillion km). Although Markarian 1 is one of the most distant galaxies ever discovered, scientists tell us that wherever there is water, there is a good possibility that life exists.

Find and circle the hidden space and science words. Look up, down, across, diagonally, and backward.

COMET	HYDROGEN	SOLAR
COSMIC	INFINITE	SPACE
DEGREE	LUNAR	STAR
ELECTRON	OXYGEN	UNIVERSE
GRAVITY	QUASAR	VACUUM

```
N  E  G  Y  X  O  L  U  X  E  I
E  L  E  C  T  R  O  N  T  O  D
G  T  U  Y  T  E  I  I  M  V  E
O  F  N  S  Z  C  N  V  P  A  R
R  K  P  R  I  I  S  E  K  C  Y
D  O  K  M  F  E  P  R  L  U  T
Y  N  S  N  E  W  A  S  S  U  I
H  O  I  R  Z  L  C  E  S  M  V
C  U  G  C  O  M  E  T  T  F  A
M  E  L  S  Y  L  U  N  A  R  R
D  X  T  Q  U  A  S  A  R  U  G
```

WHICH OF OUR SENSES CAN DETECT THE PAST?

One minute after a leaf falls or an alarm clock rings, we no longer see or hear the events. But after a breakfast of bacon and eggs, we can return hours later and still smell the aroma. This is because molecules of the food are still in the air. Like bloodhounds, we can detect the smell.

WHO MADE THE FIRST BATTERY?

Primitive batteries capable of generating one-half volt of electricity were found in Persia (now Iran and western Afghanistan) and other sites. These batteries were used over 2,000 years ago, probably to coat ornaments with silver or copper. This was done by electroplating, a method of releasing a metal from one substance and transferring it to another by an electric charge.

Do this puzzle like a regular crossword. But instead of filling in squares, put one letter in each triangle. For example, fill in the word FISH like this:

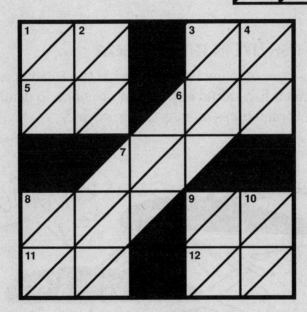

Across
1. Famous soft drink: _ _ _ _ COLA.
3. Lose color (rhymes with jade).
5. Lease.
6. A loaf of _ _ _ _ _.
7. Scottish girl.
8. Parts of flowers (rhymes with hems).
9. Adhesive _ _ _ _ (rhymes with cape).
11. Tool heated to press clothes.
12. Long jacket.

Down
1. Apple's center.
2. Short for cannot.
3. Passenger charges.
4. Not alive.
6. Large-mouthed fish (rhymes with glass).
7. Sour citrus fruit.
8. Mix.
9. Tortilla folded around a meat or cheese filling.
10. Say again: R E _ _ _ _.

WHERE THE EARTH'S LOWEST LAND REGION IS?

The shores of the Dead Sea, which form part of the border between Israel and Jordan, are 1,299 feet (396 m) below sea level. The Dead Sea itself is 1,297 feet (395 m) deep.

WHY NO FISH LIVE IN THE DEAD SEA?

No form of animal life can live in the Dead Sea. It is so salty that a fish would either float or choke to death. The Dead Sea is nine times as salty as the ocean!

Unscramble the names of these oceans and seas:

1. A D D E   __ __ __ __
   (between Israel and Jordan)

2. T R O N H   __ __ __ __ __
   (between England and Scandinavia)

3. I C F C A P I   __ __ __ __ __ __ __
   (between Asia and the Americas)

4. C A T T A L I N   __ __ __ __ __ __ __ __
   (between the Americas and
   Europe and Africa)

5. N I A D I N   __ __ __ __ __ __
   (between India and Africa)

6. C R A T I C   __ __ __ __ __ __
   (northernmost ocean)

7. E R D   __ __ __
   (between Egypt and the
   Arabian Peninsula)

8. A I N B A R A   __ __ __ __ __ __ __
   (between the Arabian Peninsula
   and India)

9. L O C A R   __ __ __ __ __
   (near eastern Australia)

10. C L A B K   __ __ __ __ __
    (near Turkey, eastern Europe, and Ukraine)

WHAT THE OLDEST LIVING THING IS?

A bristlecone pine from Nevada was tested by scientists and found to be 4,900 years old. It was a few centuries old before the first Egyptian pyramid was built!

APPLE TREES CAN PRODUCE BOTH SWEET AND SOUR APPLES?

Apple seeds usually produce trees that bear small, sour apples. To get sweet apples, new trees must be grown by planting twigs.

The answer for each numbered question is the same both across and down!

Across and Down:
1. Tree that grows from an acorn.
2. Chopping tool.
3. Small cask or barrel.

Across and Down:
1. Evergreen.
2. Excessively adored person or thing (rhymes with bridal).
3. Routine or ordinary: _ _ _ _ A L.
4. Tall shade trees that grow in a Y shape.

WHY SWISS CHEESE HAS HOLES?

In a cheese factory, workers stir harmless bacteria into vats of milk to help separate the curd (solid parts) from the whey (liquid part), which is later drained off. The stirring creates air bubbles in the curd. When the curd solidifies to become cheese the bubbles are trapped. The trapped bubbles are the holes we see when we slice the cheese.

WHAT CURDS AND WHEY ARE?

Rennet is a substance taken from the stomachs of calves and sheep. When added to milk to make cheese, the rennet acts as a curdling agent to help produce clots, or curds. The rest of the treated milk is a yellowish liquid called whey.

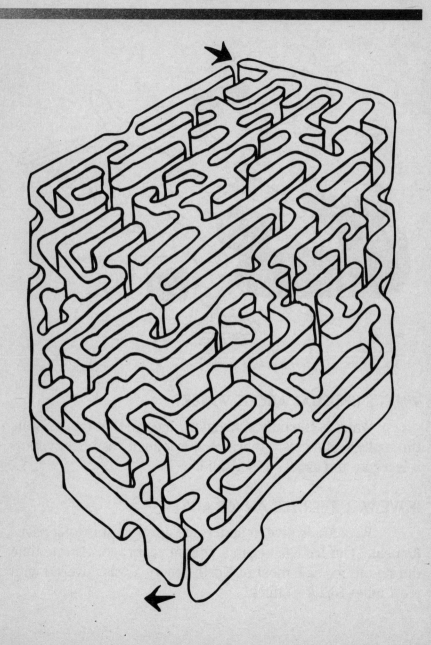

WHAT'S UNUSUAL ABOUT WATER?

Water is the only substance on earth that can exist in three physical states. As water, it is a liquid; as water vapor, it is a gas; and as ice, it is a solid.

IF WE WILL EVER SEE AN ICE AGE?

We actually live in an ice age now, but it is long past its peak. Our ice age began a million years ago. At one time during our ice age, most of North America was covered with ice 2 miles (3.2 km) thick!

Across

1. Abbreviation for postscript.
3. Colorful part of a flower.
7. Melted ice.
8. Abbreviation for absent without leave: _ _ _ L.
9. That happened a long time _ _ _.
10. Opposite of outer.
11. Second planet from the sun.
13. A kind of weasel (rhymes with vermin).
18. Star that suddenly gets very bright, then returns to normal.
20. Read quickly (rhymes with ran).
22. Roman numeral 9.
23. Ovenlike appliance used to warm homes.
25. _ _ _ _ and crafts.
26. Chews and swallows food.

Down

1. Leaf of a book.
2. Another word for rock.
3. Specially cut glass that turns light into a spectrum.
4. Some people lie on the beach to get a sun _ _ _.
5. Emotion combining admiration with wonder or dread (rhymes with raw).
6. Ruler or master.
7. Surfers ride one (rhymes with pave).
12. Seventh planet from the sun.
14. Silly (rhymes with mundane).
15. Opposite of yes.
16. Expel a tenant.
17. Washington, _ _.
19. Tools to chop with.
20. Large body of water.
21. Fore and _ _ _ (rhymes with laughed).
24. Abbreviation for anti-aircraft.

WHO INVENTED PAPER?

Thousands of years ago the Egyptians made a primitive kind of paper out of a hard-to-find plant called papyrus. But it wasn't until 105 A.D. that the Chinese discovered how to make a paper out of bark, hemp, and rags — all materials that were easily available. It was this inexpensive paper that helped spread written knowledge quickly.

WHICH REACHES THE GROUND FIRST WHEN DROPPED: A HEAVY BALL OR A LIGHT BALL?

The famous scientist Galileo dropped from a tower two objects of the same size and shape but of different weight. The heavier piece reached the ground first. In this experiment Galileo realized that the heavier object was able to move through the air more easily than the lighter object. He also determined mathematically, however, that if the balls were dropped in a vacuum (a space having no air), they would have reached the ground at the same time.

Fit the names of these famous scientists and thinkers into the puzzle. We've filled in one name to get you started.

3 letters
LEE (Chinese-born American physicist)

4 letters
BELL (Scottish-born American inventor)
BOHR (Danish physicist)
YANG (Chinese-born American physicist)

5 letters
CURIE (Polish-born French chemist and physicist)
SAGAN (American astronomer)

6 letters
FERMAT (French mathematician)
MENDEL (Austrian botanist)
NEWTON (English mathematician and scientist)

7 letters
EHRLICH (German bacteriologist)
GALILEO (Italian astronomer and physicist)

LEIBNIZ (German philosopher and mathematician)
MARCONI (Italian engineer and inventor)
MAXWELL (Scottish physicist)

8 letters
EINSTEIN (German-born American theoretical physicist)
FRANKLIN (American statesman and scientist)
LINNAEUS (Swedish botanist)

HOW MUCH SAP IS NEEDED TO MAKE A GALLON OF MAPLE SYRUP?

You must boil about 40 gallons (151 l) of sap to produce just 1 gallon (3.8 l) of maple syrup. Continued boiling past the syrup stage will make maple cream, maple butter, or sugar.

WHY HAIR IS STRAIGHT OR CURLY?

Each hair contains a shaft that determines its shape. A straight hair has a round shaft, while a curly hair has an oval or flat shaft.

Can you draw each figure making one continuous line — without lifting your pencil, crossing a line, or retracing a line?

Crystal

Saturn

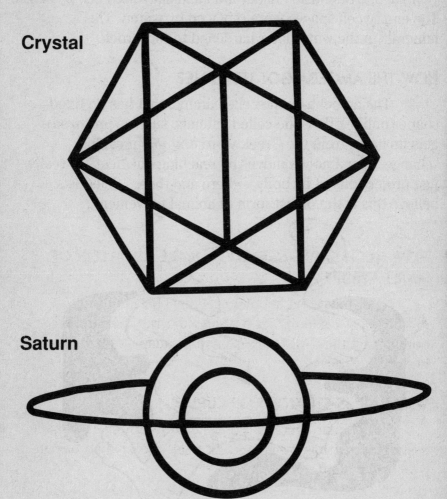

WHAT PETRIFIED WOOD IS?

Petrified wood is actually hard rock. Millions of years ago, trees buried under mud and silt rotted cell by cell. The empty cell spaces were replaced by water. The minerals in the water later hardened to form rock.

HOW THE AMOEBA GOT ITS NAME?

The amoeba, a one-celled animal that has no fixed shape (unlike other one-celled animals, such as protozoa), gets its name from the Greek word *amoibē*, meaning "change." An amoeba moves by reaching out "feet" — really just projections of its body — here and there. Scientists believe this is the oldest form of animal movement.

Starting at the top, find a path that allows you to visit all 15 chambers *only once*. On the way, gather happy cells and replace each sad cell with a happy cell. You cannot pass a room with a sad cell without replacing it. You may enter a sad-celled chamber only if it has fewer sad cells than you have happy cells. And you must end up with only one happy cell.

HOW TO TELL PLANETS AND STARS APART AT NIGHT?

There are two ways to tell planets and stars apart. First, planets shine with a steady light, while stars twinkle. Second, planets are "wanderers." They change positions in relation to the stars.

HOW FAST LIGHT TRAVELS?

If light could bend to travel around the earth, a light wave would circle the globe about seven times in 1 second!

Interplanetary Word Find • 47

Find and circle the hidden words. Look up, down, across, diagonally, and backward.

EARTH   MOON   SATELLITE
GALAXY   ORBIT   SATURN
JUPITER   PLANET   SUN
MARS   PLUTO   TELESCOPE
METEOR   RING   VENUS

```
A N Y Y H T R A E A M
R I N G N R U T A S X
W S O M Z P I V O U R
H K R V G L M O O N T
M I B T L A Q G B P R
J E I E S N L U N S E
M G T U O E D A K J T
F A N E L T F H X E I
S E R P O W U T R Y P
V Q W S A R I L D E U
L T E L E S C O P E J
```

NOT ALL BEACH SAND IS WHITE?

The Hawaiian Islands are formed mostly by a dark, heavy rock called basalt. Over many years, the Pacific Ocean has broken up some of this rock to make black sandy beaches. Basalt sand beaches are found in other places as well, such as the Canary Islands.

SOME ROCKS FLOAT?

Pumice is a rock that floats. When lava flows from a volcano, escaping gases churn the lava into a spongy froth. When the lava cools, trapped pockets of gas make the rock, now called pumice, buoyant.

Unscramble these volcano words.

1. O N O C A L V __ __ __ __ __ __ __
   (opening in the earth's surface)

2. T R E C A R __ __ __ __ __ __
   (hole of old volcano)

3. H A S __ __ __
   (pulverized residue of an eruption)

4. V A A L __ __ __ __
   (hot, flowing magma)

5. N O C E __ __ __ __
   (shape of some volcanoes)

6. G A M M A __ __ __ __ __
   (molten rock)

7. C E M U I P __ __ __ __ __ __
   (light volcanic rock that can float)

8. T R U P E __ __ __ __ __
   (explode)

9. T R U S C __ __ __ __ __
   (earth's surface)

10. L O X E N O P I S __ __ __ __ __ __ __ __ __
    (blast)

WHICH IS THE FASTEST LAND ANIMAL?

The cheetah. It can run short distances at a top speed of 70 miles (113 km) per hour. The cheetah is different from most cats because it cannot completely sheathe its claws.

WHICH IS THE HUNGRIEST ANIMAL?

The shrew, one of the tiniest mammals, has such a fast metabolic rate that it must eat almost constantly. If it goes a few hours without eating, it will starve to death.

Cross out four cheetahs so that there are only three in each row and column. Can you find at least two different ways to do it?

HOW A CAMEL SURVIVES THIRST?

A camel drinks plenty of water and eats salt before traveling. The salt helps to hold water in the animal's body tissues. The camel also uses up fat stored in its hump for food and energy. As the camel travels, water is slowly drawn off from the tissues to quench the animal's thirst. The camel can produce up to 10 gallons (38 l) of water!

WHICH IS HEAVIER — AN ELEPHANT OR A BLUE WHALE?

The blue whale's tongue alone is heavier than most elephants! The entire blue whale can weigh 150 tons (136 metric tons) compared with an elephant's 7 tons (6.4 metric tons).

Fit the names of these animals into the puzzle. We've filled in one name to get you started.

3 letters
APE
BOA
EEL
ELK
PIG

4 letters
BEAR
LION
MINK
TOAD

5 letters
CHIMP
EAGLE
LEMUR
OTTER
TIGER
WHALE

7 letters
GORILLA
LEOPARD
GIRAFFE

8 letters
ELEPHANT
KANGAROO
MONGOOSE

9 letters
ORANGUTAN

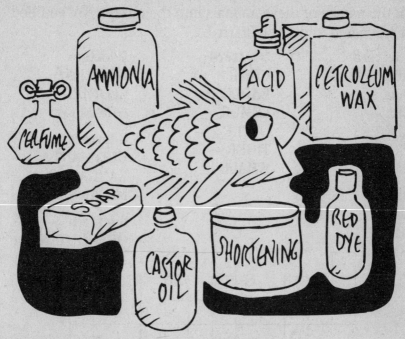

WHAT PUTS THE GLISTEN IN LIPSTICK?

Fish scales! The small shiny scales are soaked in
ammonia, then added to shortening, soap, castor oil,
petroleum wax, perfume, preservatives, acid, and other
substances. By the way, red dye gives the lipstick color, but
it's the acid that turns lips red.

WHAT A SPONGE IS?

A sponge is a sea animal. When it dies, its flesh
disappears, leaving behind the skeleton. The skeleton is the
sponge we use at home.

Find and circle the hidden words. Look up, down, across, diagonally, and backward.

BARNACLE   LOBSTER   REMORA
COCKLE   MUSSEL   SHRIMP
CRAB   OCTOPUS   SPONGE
CUTTLEFISH   OYSTER   SQUID
KRILL   PRAWN   STARFISH

```
P  M  I  R  H  S  F  F  Y  P  A
E  B  A  A  R  O  M  E  R  R  C
L  L  E  S  S  U  M  A  E  T  U
C  O  C  K  L  E  W  T  A  W  T
A  L  E  M  Y  N  S  S  P  N  T
N  M  C  R  A  B  L  Z  D  I  L
R  D  S  P  O  N  G  E  U  X  E
A  I  Z  L  R  E  T  S  Y  O  F
B  U  O  C  T  O  P  U  S  R  I
R  Q  N  T  X  L  L  I  R  K  S
Q  S  O  S  T  A  R  F  I  S  H
```

WHAT'S UNUSUAL ABOUT THE STRAWBERRY?

It's not a berry at all! In fact, the strawberry belongs to the rose family. Unlike a true berry, such as the blueberry, the strawberry has no outer skin around the seed. Instead, the strawberry has a fleshy, swollen fruit with dry yellow seeds on the outside. At one time it was called a strewberry because the berries seemed to be strewn about the leaves of the plant.

WHY WE YAWN?

When we're tired or bored, a good yawn brings in extra oxygen that perks us up and keeps us awake.

Do this puzzle like a regular crossword. But instead of filling in squares, put one letter in each triangle. For example, fill in the word LION like this:

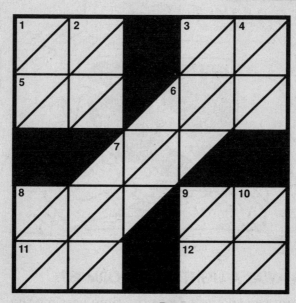

Across

1. The highest point (rhymes with hackney).
3. Dressed (rhymes with bad).
5. Cure.
6. Streets.
7. Drench in water.
8. Engine (rhymes with rotor).
9. Destiny (rhymes with late).
11. Pep up (rhymes with lurk).
12. Sharp (rhymes with bean).

Down

1. Too much candy gave him a TOOTH_ _ _ _.
2. Food served and eaten in one sitting (rhymes with wheel).
3. Cape (rhymes with joke).
4. Totals.
6. Lion's noise.
7. Long-legged bird (rhymes with pork).
8. To be gloomy and listless (rhymes with hope).
9. Phony.
10. Adolescent.

HOW FAR AWAY A LIGHTNING STORM IS?

Count the seconds from the time you see the lightning flash until you hear the first thunder boom, then divide by 5. Sound travels about 1 mile (1.6 km) every 5 seconds, so a count of 5 from flash to boom means the storm is only 1 mile (1.6 km) away.

HOW LONG A LIGHTNING BOLT IS?

An average bolt is 3 miles (4.8 km) long. But many bolts reach a length of up to 10 miles (16 km).

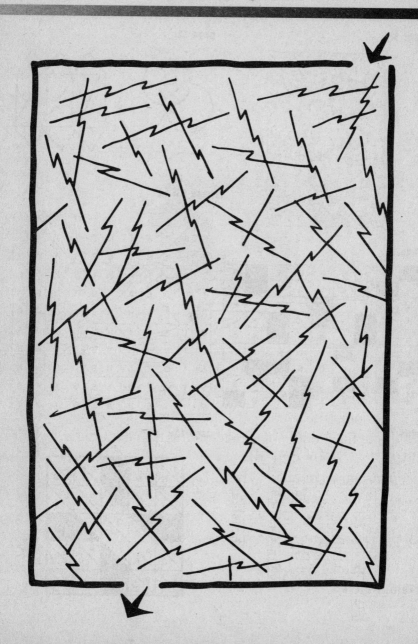

page 5:

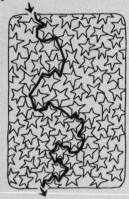

page 11:

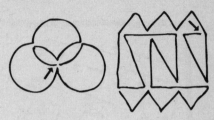

page 13:

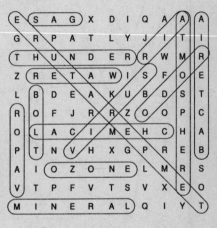

page 7:

page 9:

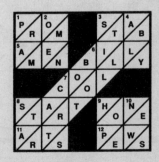

page 15:

page 17:

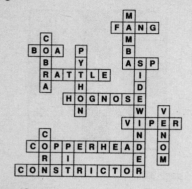

page 19:

1. SALTY
2. RAIN
3. SNOW
4. WAVE
5. TIDE
6. SEA
7. ICE
8. VAPOR
9. HARD
10. SOFT
11. WET
12. SPRING

page 21:

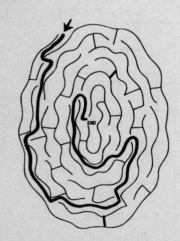

page 23:

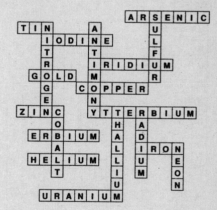

page 25:

page 27:

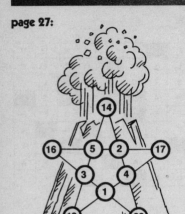

page 29:

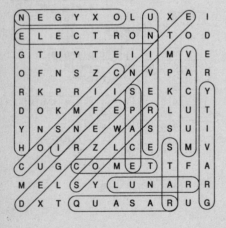

page 31:

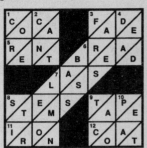

page 33:

1. DEAD	6. ARCTIC
2. NORTH	7. RED
3. PACIFIC	8. ARABIAN
4. ATLANTIC	9. CORAL
5. INDIAN	10. BLACK

page 35:

O	A	K
A	X	E
K	E	G

P	I	N	E
I	D	O	L
N	O	R	M
E	L	M	S

page 37:

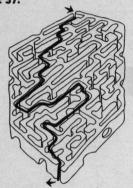

page 39:

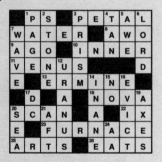

page 41:

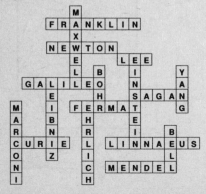

page 43:

page 45:

page 47:

64 • Answers

1. VOLCANO
2. CRATER
3. ASH
4. LAVA
5. CONE
6. MAGMA
7. PUMICE
8. ERUPT
9. CRUST
10. EXPLOSION

pages 51:

Here are four possible answers:

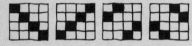

page 53:

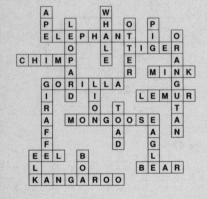

page 55:

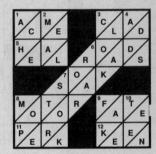

page 57:

page 59: